P9-AZX-527

The fly was buzzing around.
Frog sat very still on his lily pad
in the middle of the pond.

The fly buzzed and buzzed around Frog.

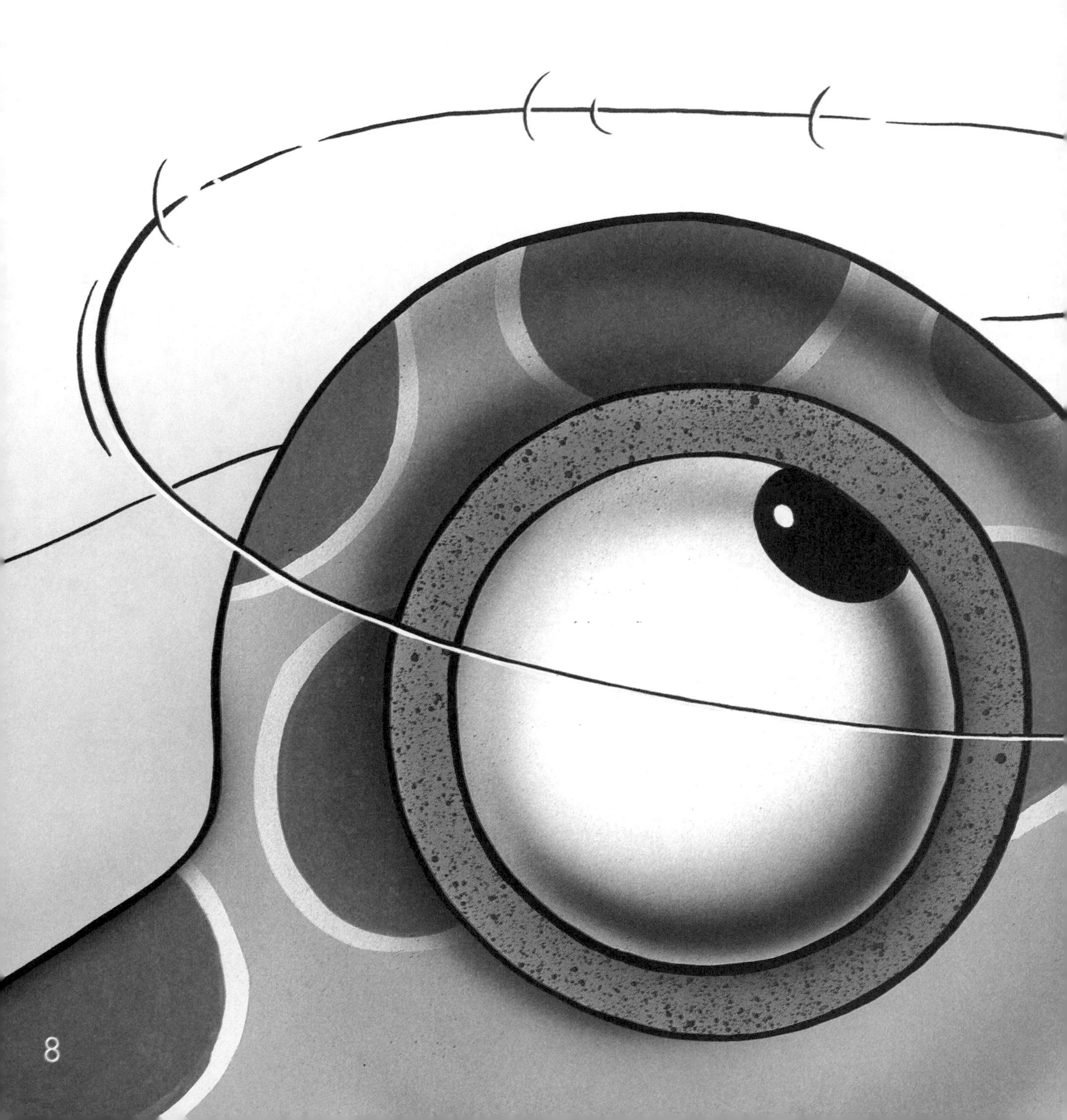

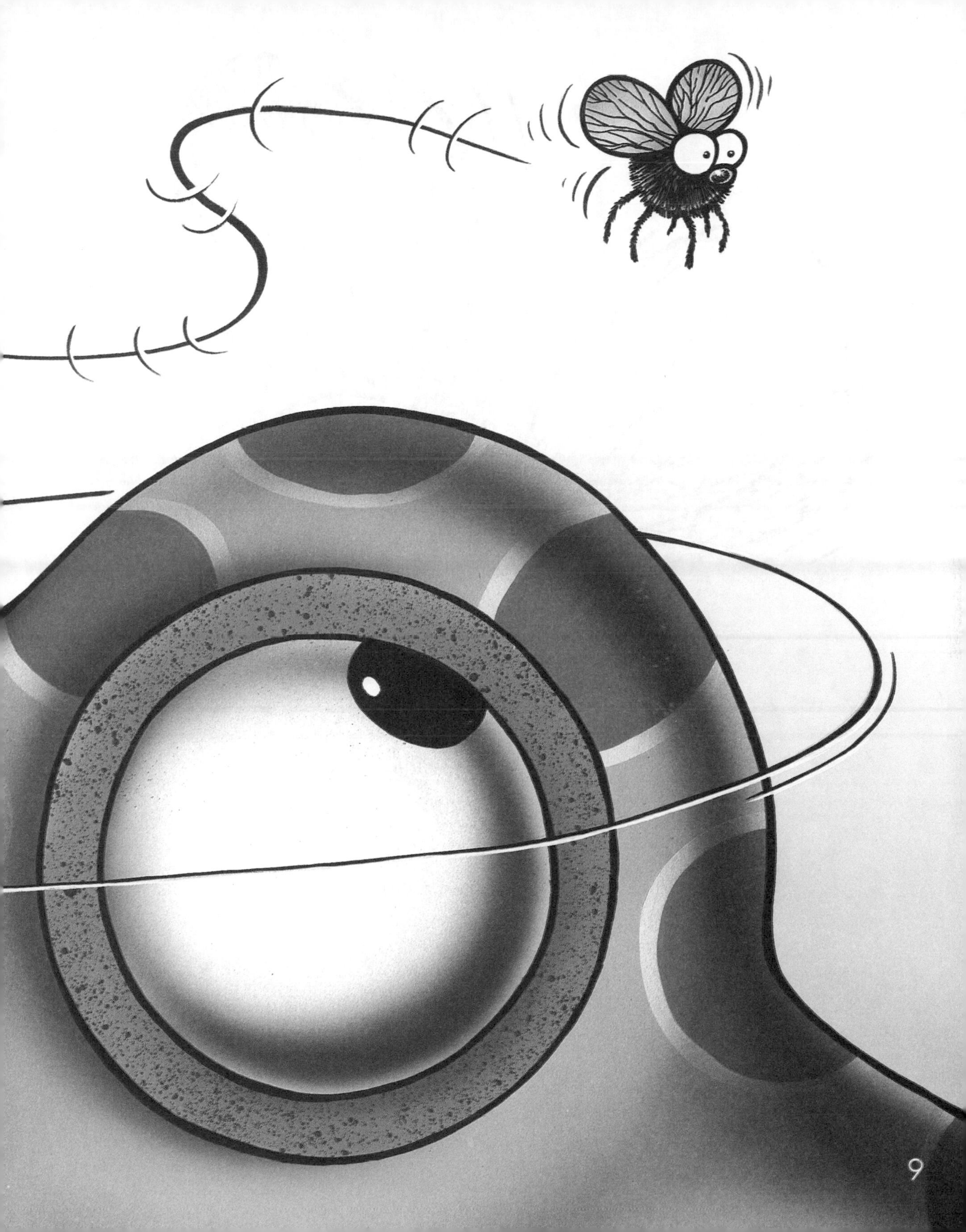

"Buzz buzz," said the fly.

Frog sat very, very still.

"Buzz buzz," said the fly.

Frog's eyes grew big.
The fly came closer and closer to Frog.

Snap!

Frog snapped up the fly.

"Mmmm," said Frog.
"Good lunch!"